Mermaids

Mermaids

An Anthology of Verse and Prose

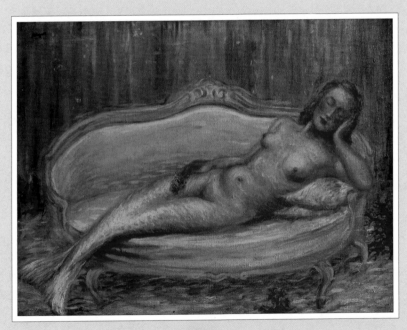

SMITHMARK

This edition published in 1996 by
Smithmark Publishers, a division of U.S. Media Holdings Inc.,
16 East 32nd Street, New York, NY 10016

Smithmark books are available for bulk purchase for sales promotion and for premium use. For details
write or call the Manager of Special Sales, SMITHMARK Publishers, 16 East 32nd Street, New York, NY
10016; (212) 532-6600.

Produced by Anness Publishing Limited
1 Boundary Row
London SE1 8HP

10 9 8 7 6 5 4 3 2 1

Printed in Singapore by Star Standard Industries Pte. Ltd.

CONTENTS

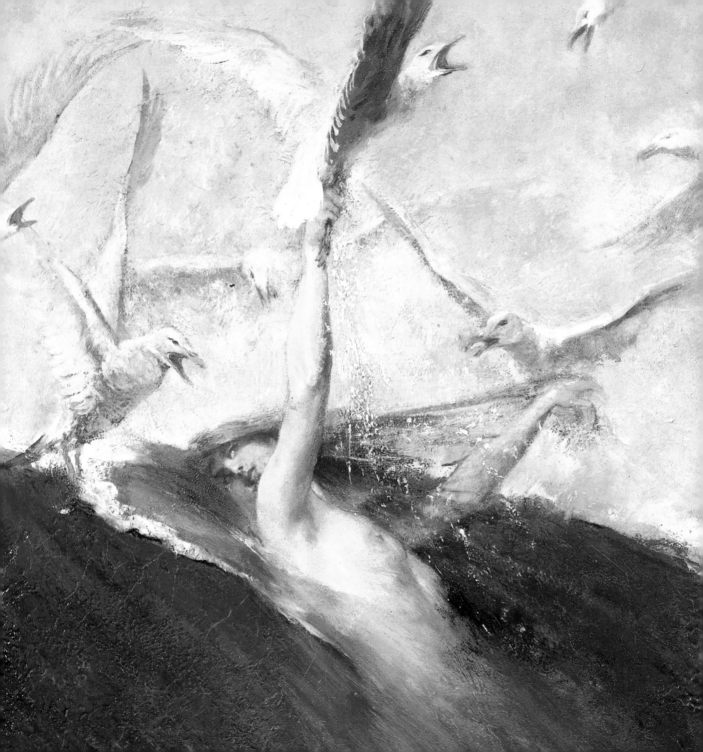

Chapter One

Maidens of Mystery, Love & Pain

Lorelei

DOWN THE GREEN WATERS came the boatman's frail craft, ever drawing nearer to the perilous rock. All his care and all his skill were required to avert a very visible danger. But high above him, from the rock round which the swirling eddies splashed and foamed, there came a voice.

> "Her voice was like the voice the stars
> Had when they sang together."

And when the boatman looked up at the sound of such sweet music, he beheld a maiden more fair than any he had ever dreamed of. On the rock she sat, combing her long golden hair with a comb of red gold. Her limbs were white as foam and her eyes green like the emerald green of the rushing river. And her red lips smiled on him and her arms were held out to him in welcome, and the sound of her song thrilled through the heart of him who listened, and her eyes drew his soul to her arms.

Forgotten was all peril. The rushing stream seized the little boat and did with it as it willed. And while the boatman still gazed upwards, intoxicated by her matchless beauty and the magic of her voice, his boat was swept against the rock, and, with the jar and crash, knowledge came back to him, and he heard, with broken heart, the mocking laughter of the Lorelei as he was dragged down as if by a thousand icy hands, and, with a choking sigh, surrendered his life to the pitiless river.

JEAN LANG, *A Book of Myths*

HE KNEW THAT he was being watched. It was not at all a frightening sensation, but one that made him intensely curious. He looked right and left, and up towards the dim roof, and down upon the yellow floor, and then, all at once, glanced quickly towards the opposite wall of the cavern.

Two big eyes, clear and green as sea waves, were peering down at him from behind an overhanging ledge of rock.

Val jumped up, startled certainly, but not frightened. The eyes had disappeared, but he stood still on the floor of the cave with his hands in his pockets, and called:

'Who's up there? Come out! I won't hurt you!' he said, as valiantly as though he had been fourteen, instead of four feet high.

There was no reply at first, but just as he was wondering whether he could climb up the face of the rock and look over, a little head slowly rose above the ledge, and then a pair of slender white shoulders, till half the body of a little girl was visible.

Was it a little girl? Val, standing open-mouthed below, thought her at any rate the strangest he had ever seen.

She had long hair, from which the water dripped, hanging straight on either side of her little face; but it was green hair, something like the seaweed which clothed the rock, only finer

and prettier. Her eyes were green too, but clear translucent green, like the sea where it is very deep and still. She had a tiny wistful face, white and childish, and a pretty mouth whose lips were only faintly touched with pink.

'I say!' cried Val, when he had a little recovered from his astonishment. 'I'm so glad you're here. Come down. I want to talk to you!'

'I – I can't,' said the little girl plaintively, and her voice was like the murmuring of the waves outside.

'Why not? I'll help you,' Val declared. 'Put one foot on the ledge, and the other –'

'I haven't any feet,' she interrupted, and two tears slowly gathered in her eyes.

'Oh! I say, you know!' began Val dubiously. 'How did you get up there, then?'

'I – I swam in when the tide was high, and – and I was playing on the ledge, and the sea went away and left me here,' she answered in a mournful voice.

Val gasped. 'Are you a – a mermaid?' he asked breathlessly. It seemed too good to be true.

'Y-yes,' sobbed the poor little sea child. 'I have a f-fish's tail.' She dragged herself closer to the ledge, and Val saw that her tiny body ended in a curved and tapering tail.

'How jolly !' he murmured with admiration.

NETTA SYRETT, *A Sea Child*

THEY WERE FAIRE LADIES, till they fondly striv'd
With th' Heliconian maides for maystery;
Of whom they, over-comen, were depriv'd
Of their proud beautie, and th' one moyity
Transform'd to fish for their bold surquedry;
But th' upper halfe their hew retayned still,
And their sweet skill in wonted melody;
Which ever after they abused to ill,
T' allure weake traveillers, whom gotten they did kill.

from EDMUND SPENSER, *The Faerie Queene*

The Mermaid

ONE FRIDAY MORN when we set sail,
And our ship not far from land,
We there did espy a pretty fair maid,
With a comb and a glass in her hand.
While the raging seas did roar,
And the stormy winds did blow,
And we jolly sailor-boys were all up aloft
And the land-lubbers lying down below.

ANON.

Every evening he went out upon the sea, and one evening the net was so heavy that hardly could he draw it into the boat. And he laughed, and said to himself, 'Surely I have caught all the fish that swim, or snared some dull monster that will be a marvel to men, or some thing of horror that the great Queen will desire,' and putting forth all his strength, he tugged at the coarse ropes till, like lines of blue enamel round a vase of bronze, the long veins rose up on his arms. He tugged at the thin ropes, and nearer and nearer came the circle of flat corks, and the net rose at last to the top of the water.

But no fish at all was in it, nor any monster or thing of horror, but only a little Mermaid lying fast asleep.

Her hair was as a wet fleece of gold, and each separate hair as a thread of fine gold in a cup of glass. Her body was as white ivory, and her tail was of silver and pearl. Silver and pearl was her tail, and the green weeds of the sea coiled round it; and like sea-shells were her ears, and her lips were like sea-coral. The cold waves dashed over her cold breasts, and the salt glistened upon her eyelids.

So beautiful was she that when the young Fisherman saw her he was filled with wonder, and he put out his hand and drew the net close to him, and leaning over the side he clasped her in his arms. And when he touched her, she gave a cry like a startled sea-gull, and woke, and looked at him in terror with her mauve-amethyst eyes, and struggled that she might escape. But he held her tightly to him, and would not suffer her to depart.

OSCAR WILDE, *The Fisherman and his Soul*

'DIDN'T I SAY that fish would be delicious?' she cried; and plunging her spoon into the dish the girl helped herself to a large piece. But the instant it touched her mouth a cold shiver ran through her. Her head seemed to flatten, and her eyes to look oddly round the corners; her legs and her arms were stuck to her sides, and she gasped wildly for breath. With a mighty bound she sprang through the window and fell into the river, where she soon felt better, and was able to swim to the sea, which was close by.

No sooner had she arrived there than the sight of her sad face attracted the notice of some of the other fishes, and they pressed round her, begging her to tell them her story.

'I am not a fish at all,' said the new-comer, swallowing a great deal of salt water as she spoke; for you cannot learn how to be a proper fish all in a moment. 'I am not a fish at all, but a girl; at least I was a girl a few minutes ago, only -' And she ducked her head under the waves so that they should not see her crying.

ANDREW LANG, *The Girl-Fish*

The Maid of the Sea

COME FROM the sea,
Maiden, to me,
Maiden of mystery, love, and pain!
Wake from thy sleep,
Low in the deep,
Over thy green waves sport again!
Come to this sequestered spot, love,
Death's where thou art, as where thou art not, love;
Then come unto me,
Maid of the Sea,
Rise from the wild and stormy main:
Wake from thy sleep,
Calm in the deep,
Over thy green waves sport again!

JAMES HOGG

'IT WAS CALM ENOUGH that night Anthony O'Flaherty was here, and there was a moon shining, pretty near a full moon, so Anthony could see plain. Well, there was three of them in it, and they were playing among themselves.'

'Mermaids?'

This time my voice expressed full sympathy. The sea all round us was rising in queer round little waves, though there was no wind. The boom snatched at the blocks as the boat rocked. The sail was ghostly white. The vision of a mermaid would not have surprised me greatly.

'The beautifullest ever was seen,' said Peter, 'with neither shift nor shirt on them, only just themselves, and the long hair of them. Straight it was and black, only for a taste of green in it… Once Anthony had seen them, he couldn't rest content without he'd be going to see them again. Many a night he went and saw neither sight nor light of them, for it was only at spring tides that they'd be there, on account of the rocks not being uncovered any other time. But at the bottom of the low springs they were there right enough, and sometimes they'd be swimming in the sea and sometimes they'd be sitting on the rocks. It was wonderful the songs they'd sing – like the sound of the sea set to music was what my mother told me, and she was told by them that knew. The people did be wondering what had come over Anthony, for he was different like from what he had been, and nobody knew what took him out of his house in the middle of the night at the spring tides. There was a girl that they had laid down for him to marry, and Anthony had no objection to her before he had seen them ones; but after he had seen them he wouldn't look at the girl…'

GEORGE A. BIRMINGHAM, *The Mermaid*

The Birth of Venus

VENUS (Dione, Aphrodite, Cytherea), the goddess of beauty, love, laughter and marriage, is by some said to be the daughter of Jupiter and Dione, goddess of moisture; others report that she sprang from the foam of the sea.

> "LOOK, LOOK, why shine
>   Those floating bubbles with such light divine?
>   They break, and from their mist a lily form
>   Rises from out the wave, in beauty warm.
>   The wave is by the blue-veined feet scarce press'd,
>   Her silky ringlets float about her breast,
>   Veiling its fairy loveliness; while her eye
>   Is soft and deep as the blue heaven is high.
>   The Beautiful is born; and sea and earth
>   May well revere the hour of that mysterious birth."

SHELLEY

THE OCEAN NYMPHS were the first to discover her, cradled on a great blue wave; and they carried her down into their coral caves, where they tenderly nursed her, and taught her with the utmost care. Then, her education being completed, the sea nymphs judged it time to introduce her to the other gods, and, with that purpose in view, carried her up to the surface of the sea, — where Tritons, Oceanides and Nereides all crowded around her, loudly expressing their ardent admiration, — and offered her pearls and choice bits of coral from the deep, as a tribute to her charms.

Then they pillowed her softly on a great wave, and entrusted her to the care of Zephyrus, the soft south wind, who blew a gentle breath, and wafted her to the Island of Cyprus.

H. A. GUERBER, *The Myths of Greece and Rome*

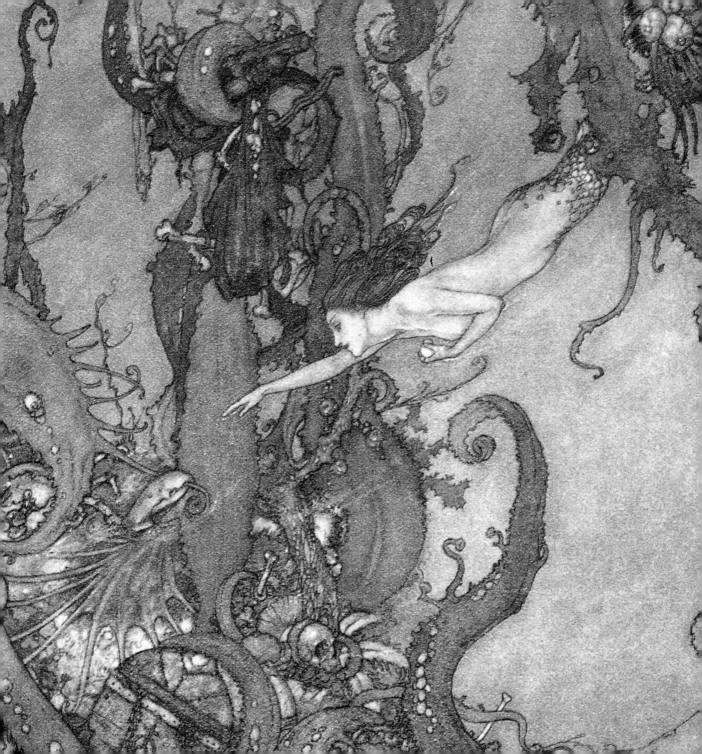

CHAPTER TWO

Silent Grottos and Coral Caves

The Mermaid

I

WHO WOULD BE a mermaid fair,
Singing alone, combing her hair,
Under the sea, in a golden curl,
With a comb of pearl,
On a throne?

II

I WOULD BE a mermaid fair.
I would sing to myself the whole of the day;
With a comb of pearl I would comb my hair;
And still as I comb'd I would sing and say,
'Who is it loves me? who loves not me?'
I would comb my hair till my ringlets would fall
Low adown, low adown,
From under my starry sea-bud crown
Low adown and around;
And I should look like a fountain of gold
Springing alone
With a shrill inner sound,
Over the throne
In the midst of the hall;
Till that great sea-snake under the sea
From his coiled sleeps in the central deeps
Would slowly trail himself sevenfold
Round the hall where I sate, and look in at the gate
With his large calm eyes for the love of me.
And all the mermen under the sea
Would feel their immortality
Die in their hearts for the love of me.

ALFRED, LORD TENNYSON

IT WAS A SPLENDID SIGHT, such as is never seen on earth. The walls and the ceiling of the great dancing-saloon were of thick but transparent glass. Several hundreds of huge shells, pink and grass-green, stood on each side in rows, filled with a blue fire which lit up the whole hall and shone through the walls, so that the sea without was quite lit up; one could see all the innumerable fishes, great and small, swimming towards the glass walls; of some the scales gleamed with purple, while in others they shone like silver and gold. Through the midst of the hall flowed a broad stream, and on this the sea men and sea women danced to their own charming songs. Such beautiful voices the people of the earth have not. The little sea maid sang the most sweetly of all, and the whole court applauded her, and for a moment she felt gay in

her heart, for she knew that she had the loveliest voice of all in the sea
or on the earth. But soon again she thought of the world above her.
She could not forget the handsome Prince, and her sorrow at not
possessing an immortal soul. Then she stole out of her father's palace,
and whilst all within was merriment and happiness, she sat in deep
sorrow in her little garden. She now heard a horn sound through
water, and she thought, 'That is no doubt the Prince sailing there
above, he for whom all my desires centre, and in whose hands I
would trust my life's happiness. I will venture everything to gain him
and an immortal soul. Whilst my sisters are dancing I will go to the
Water-witch, of whom I have always been so afraid; but she can,
perhaps, advise and help me.'

HANS ANDERSEN, *The Little Sea Maid*

Sunk Lyonesse

IN SEA-COLD LYONESSE,
When the Sabbath eve shafts down
On the roofs, walls, belfries
Of the foundered town,
The Nereids pluck their lyres
Where the green translucency beats,
And with motionless eyes at gaze
Make minstrelsy in the streets.

AND THE ocean water stirs
In salt-worn casement and porch.
Plies the blunt-snouted fish
With fire in his skull for torch.
And the ringing wires resound;
And the unearthly lovely weep,
In lament of the music they make
In the sullen courts of sleep:
Whose marble flowers bloom for aye:
And — lapped by the moon-guiled tide —
Mock their carver with heart of stone,
Caged in his stone-ribbed side.

WALTER DE LA MARE

IN THE DEEP CAVERNS of the sea there dwelt a
sea-king who had a mortal woman for his
wife. He loved her dearly and devotedly, and
she loved him in return, and for a long while
they lived happily together in their palace
under the sea with their children, who were all
little mermen and mermaidens. The caverns
of the sea palace were cool and beautiful,
ceilinged with amber, paved with pearl, and
filled with soft, dim lights. Outside the cavern
doors the many-coloured seaweeds waved to
and fro with the tide, and under their shadow
the little mermen and mermaidens played
with the sea beasts and the fishes and watched
the sea snakes coil and twine and the great
whales go sailing by on their journey round
the world.

CHRISTINE CHAUNDLER, *The Forsaken Merman*

Full fathom five thy father lies;
Of his bones are coral made:
Those are pearls that were his eyes:
Nothing of him that doth fade,
But doth suffer a sea-change
Into something rich and strange.
Sea-nymphs hourly ring his knell:
Ding-dong.
Hark! now I hear them,—
Ding-dong, bell.

WILLIAM SHAKESPEARE, from *The Tempest*

CHAPTER THREE

The Wild Notes Swell

A Sea-Spell

HER LUTE hangs shadowed in the apple-tree,
　While flashing fingers weave the sweet-strung spell
　Between its chords; and as the wild notes swell,
The sea-bird for those branches leaves the sea.
But to what sound her listening ear stoops she?
　What netherworld gulf-whispers doth she hear,
　In answering echoes from what planisphere,
Along the wind, along the estuary?

SHE SINKS into her spell: and when full soon
　Her lips move and she soars into her song,
　What creatures of the midmost main shall throng
In furrowed surf-clouds to the summoning rune:
Till he, the fated mariner, hears her cry,
And up her rock, bare-breasted, comes to die?

D. G. ROSSETTI

Guyon and the Mermaids

THEY CAME THEN to a peaceful bay that lay in the shadow of a great grey hill, and from it came the sweetest music that Guyon had ever heard.

Five beautiful mermaids were swimming in the clear green water, and the melody of their song made Guyon long to stop and listen. They had made this song about Guyon:

> O THOU FAIR SON of gentle fairy,
> Thou art in mighty arms most magnified
> Above all knights that ever battle tried.
> O! turn thy rudder hitherward awhile,
> Here may thy storm-beat vessel safely ride.
> This is the port of rest from troublous toil,
> The world's sweet inn from pain and wearisome turmoil.

The rolling sea gently echoed their music, and the breaking waves kept time with their voices. The very wind seemed to blend with the melody and make it so beautiful that Guyon longed and longed to go with them to their peaceful bay under the grey hill. But the palmer would not let him stop, and the boatman rowed onwards.

JEANIE LANG, *The Quest of Sir Guyon*

The Sirens

COME TO THE LAND where none grows old,
And none is rash or over-bold,
Nor any noise there is or war,
Or rumour from wild lands afar,
Or plagues, or birth and death of kings;
No vain desire of unknown things
Shall vex you there, no hope or fear
Of that which never draweth near;
But in that lovely land and still
Ye may remember what ye will,
And what ye will, forget for aye.
So while the kingdoms pass away,
Ye sea-beat hardened toilers erst,
Unresting, for vain fame athirst,
Shall be at peace for evermore,
With hearts fulfilled of Godlike lore,
And calm, unwavering Godlike love,
No lapse of time can turn or move.
There, ages after your fair fleece
Is clean forgotten, yea, and Greece
Is no more counted glorious,
Alone with us, alone with us,
Alone with us, dwell happily,
Beneath our trembling roof of sea.

WILLIAM MORRIS, *The Life and Death of Jason*

THE SIRENS were lovely sea-nymphs, who, by means of their sweet singing, enticed travellers to draw too near the rocks so that either their ships were dashed to pieces, or they themselves were filled with such a longing to be with these beautiful maidens that they sprang over the sides of their vessels and were drowned in the raging sea. No one could listen to the magic songs of the Sirens without doing themselves some harm.

Now, Circe had warned Ulysses about the Sirens; and so he prepared for this danger in good time. He closed up the ears of his companions with melted wax, so that they would not be able to hear the magic song; and then, as they drew near to the place of danger, he made them bind him fast with leather cords to the mast of his ship so that he could not possibly break away, and told them not to set him free until he made signs to them that the sound of the singing could no longer be heard.

This clever plan met with great success; for when the ships came in sight of the enchanted island, upon the dangerous rocks of which the Sirens sat, combing out their long shining hair, the travellers could not hear the enticing songs they sang, and so had no wish to draw nearer or to throw themselves into the sea.

But Ulysses himself passed through awful hours of woe and pain; for as he heard the thrilling songs of the sweet-voiced Sirens, he was filled with a terrible longing to fling himself into the sea that he might reach the lovely enchantresses. But though he struggled furiously to break his leather cords, and called out wildly to be set free, his faithful companions obeyed the command he had given them before they reached the enchanted rocks. Unable themselves to hear the thrilling song of the Sirens, they paid no heed to the cries of their leader, but rowed hard until the island was lost in the distance.

GLADYS DAVIDSON, The Wanderings of Ulysses

Lorelei

A SADNESS its shadow is flinging
Around me I know not why;
My haunted memory ringing
With a lay of the days gone by.

THE BREEZE is cool, it grows darkling,
And the Rhine doth noiseless run;
The mountain-summits are sparkling
In the rays of the evening sun.

HIGH YONDER in wondrous seeming,
Reclines a maiden fair,
Her golden jewels are gleaming
And she combs her golden hair.

A COMB OF GOLD is she plying
And warbles a wondrous song,
That a thrilling melody sighing,
Floats like a spell along.

THE BOATMAN his bark while steering,
Is seized with a wild amaze;
He heeds not the rocks that are nearing,
Fixed high is his spell-bound gaze.

AND SOON by the waters swallowed,
Will bark and boatman lie;
Such fatal charm weaves ever
The song of the Lorelei.

HEINRICH HEINE (TRANS. STRATHEIR)

'LISTEN!' said the Wind-fairy. 'Don't you hear someone singing?'
Jack listened, and heard a sad sweet voice singing a song, which was more beautiful than anything he had ever heard before.

'That is a mermaid,' said the Wind-fairy, 'and she is singing to a ship. She will go on singing until the ship follows the sound. Then she will gradually lead it down into a whirlpool, and there it will be swallowed up, and the poor sailors will never return to their wives and little children. But I will go and blow the ship in another direction, whether it likes it or no, until it is out of the sound of her song, and then it will go on all right. Ah! men little think, when they complain of meeting gales of wind, that it is often for their own good, and that we are blowing them away from danger, not into it.'

'A mermaid!' cried Jack. 'I have never seen one. How much I should like to see her!'

'When we have gone to the ship we will go and look at her,' said the Wind-fairy. Then he flew to one side, till they came to a ship full of sailors sailing quietly along, and the Wind-fairy began to blow with all his might. He blew till the sea rose in great heavy waves. The ship leaned over on one side. The captain shouted. The sailors threw up the ropes, and all trembled for fear. But much against their will the ship had to be turned about and go in another direction, and the Wind-fairy never left off blowing till she was many miles away from the sound of the mermaid's song.

'Now we will go and look at the mermaid,' said he; and back they flew again to the same spot. There, beneath them, resting on the top of the waves, Jack saw a very beautiful maiden. She had sad green eyes and long green hair. When he looked closer he saw that she had a long bright tail instead of legs, but he thought her very beautiful all the same. She was still singing in a sad sleepy voice, and as he listened he began to long to jump into the sea beside her. And the longing grew so strong that he would have thrown himself into her arms at once, had not the Wind-fairy seized him and flown off with him before he had time.

MARY DE MORGAN, *Through the Fire*

SINCE ONCE I sat upon a promontory,
And heard a maiden on a dolphin's back
Uttering such dulcet and harmonious breath,
That the rude sea grew civil at her song,
And certain stars shot madly from their spheres,
To hear the sea-maid's music.

WILLIAM SHAKESPEARE, *A Midsummer Night's Dream*

CHAPTER FOUR

Go Up, Dear Heart, Through the Waves

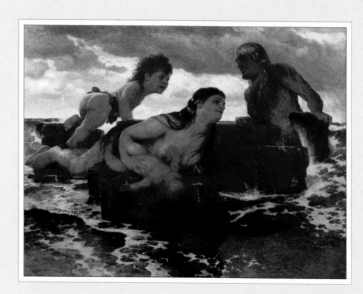

WHO ARE THEY, O pensive Graces,
– For I dreamed they wore your forms –
Who on shores and sea-wash'd places
Scoop the shelves and fret the storms?
Who, when ships are that way tending,
Troop across the flushing sands,
To all reefs and narrows wending,
With blown tresses, and with beckoning hands?

MATTHEW ARNOLD, from The New Sirens

Oh ye! who have your eye-balls vexed and tired,
Feast them upon the wideness of the Sea;
Oh ye! whose ears are dinned with uproar rude,
Or fed too much with cloying melody, —
Sit ye near some old cavern's mouth, and brood
Until ye start, as if the sea-nymphs quired!

JOHN KEATS, from *On the Sea*

Sailor's Song

TO SEA, TO SEA! The calm is o'er;
The wanton water leaps in sport,
And rattles down the pebbly shore;
The dolphin wheels, the sea-cows snort,
And unseen mermaids' pearly song
Comes bubbling up, the weeds among.
Fling broad the sail, dip deep the oar:
To sea, to sea! The calm is o'er.

TO SEA, TO SEA! Our wide-winged bark
Shall billowy cleave its sunny way,
And with its shadow, fleet and dark,
Break the caved Tritons' azure day,
Like mighty eagle soaring light
O'er antelopes on Alpine height.
The anchor heaves, the ship swings free,
The sails swell full. To sea, to sea!

THOMAS LOVELL BEDDOES

THE VESSEL had not gone very far when she ran upon a rock, and stuck so fast in a cleft that the strength of the whole crew could not get her off again. To make matters worse, the wind was rising too, and it was quite plain that in a few hours the ship would be dashed to pieces and everybody would be drowned, when suddenly the form of a mermaid was seen dancing on the waves which threatened every moment to overwhelm them.

'There is only one way to free yourselves,' she said to the king, bobbing up and down in the water as she spoke, 'and that is to give me your solemn word that you will deliver to me the first child that is born to you.'

The king hesitated at this proposal. He hoped that some day he might have children in his home, and the thought that he must yield up the heir to his crown was very bitter to him; but just then a huge wave broke with great force on the ship's side, and his men fell on their knees and entreated him to save them.

So he promised, and this time a wave lifted the vessel clean off the rocks, and she was in the open sea once more.

ANDREW LANG, *The Mermaid and the Boy*

Mermaidens' Vesper-Hymn

TROOP HOME to silent grots and caves!
Troop home! And mimic as you go
The mournful winding of the waves
Which to their dark abysses flow.

AT THIS sweet hour, all things beside
In amorous pairs to covert creep;
The swans that brush the evening tide
Homeward in snowy couples keep.

IN HIS green den the murmuring seal
Close by his sleek companion lies;
While singly we to bedward steal,
And close in fruitless sleep our eyes.

IN BOWERS of love men take their rest,
In loveless bowers we sigh alone,
With bosom-friends are others blest, —
But we have none! but we have none!

GEORGE DARLEY

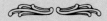

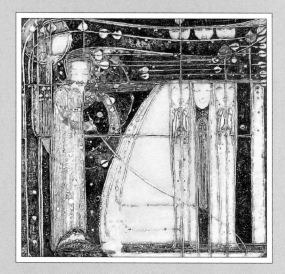

COME, DEAR CHILDREN, come away down;
Call no more!
One last look at the white-wall'd town,
And the little grey church on the windy shore,
Then come down!
She will not come though you call all day;
Come away, come away!

CHILDREN DEAR, was it yesterday
(Call yet once) that she went away?
Once she sate with you and me,
On a red gold throne in the heart of the sea,
And the youngest sate on her knee.
She comb'd its bright hair, and she tended it well,
When down swung the sound of a far-off bell.
She sigh'd, she look'd up through the clear green sea;
She said: 'I must go, for my kinsfolk pray
In the little grey church on the shore today.
'Twill be Easter-time in the world — ah me!
And I lose my poor soul, Merman! here with thee.'
I said: 'Go up, dear heart, through the waves;
Say thy prayer, and come back to the kind sea-caves!'
She smiled, she went up through the surf in the bay.
Children dear, was it yesterday?'

MATTHEW ARNOLD, from *The Forsaken Merman*

The Ballad of the Boat

THE STREAM was smooth as glass, we said: 'Arise, and let's away;'
The Siren sang beside the boat that in the rushes lay,
And spread the sail, and strong the oar, we gaily took our way.
When shall the sandy bar be cross'd? When shall we find the bay?

The broadening flood swells slowly out o'er cattle-dotted plains;
The stream is strong and turbulent, and dark with heavy rains;
The labourer looks up to see our shallop speed away.
When shall the sandy bar be cross'd? When shall we find the bay?

Now are the clouds like fiery shrouds; the sun superbly large,
Slow as an oak to woodman's stroke sinks flaming at their marge;
The waves are bright with mirror'd light as jacinths on our way.
When shall the sandy bar be cross'd? When shall we find the bay?

The moon is high up in the sky, and now no more we see
The spreading river's either bank, and surging distantly
There booms a sullen thunder as of breakers far away,
Now shall the sandy bar be cross'd, now shall we find the bay.

The sea-gull shrieks high overhead, and dimly to our sight
The moonlit crests of foaming waves gleam towering through the night.
We'll steal upon the mermaid soon, and start her from her lay,
When once the sandy bar is cross'd, and we are in the bay.

What rises white and awful, as a shroud-enfolded ghost?
What roar of rampant tumult bursts in clangour on the coast?
Pull back! Pull back! The raging flood sweeps every oar away.
O stream, is this thy bar of sand? O boat, is this the bay?

DR RICHARD GARNETT

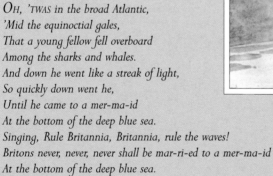

OH, 'TWAS in the broad Atlantic,
'Mid the equinoctial gales,
That a young fellow fell overboard
Among the sharks and whales.
And down he went like a streak of light,
So quickly down went he,
Until he came to a mer-ma-id
At the bottom of the deep blue sea.
Singing, Rule Britannia, Britannia, rule the waves!
Britons never, never, never shall be mar-ri-ed to a mer-ma-id
At the bottom of the deep blue sea.

ANON., *Oh! 'Twas in the Broad Atlantic*

A MERMAID *found a swimming lad,*
Picked him for her own,
Pressed her body to his body,
Laughing; and plunging down
Forgot in cruel happiness
That even lovers drown.

W. B. YEATS, *The Mermaid*

Acknowledgements

The Publishers gratefully acknowledge the following picture agencies for permission to use their pictures in this book.

The Bridgeman Art Library, London.

p1 and p 62 *Opera Dresses* from Nikolaus Heideloff's 'Gallery of Fashion' Vol II, June 1796, Private collection. p2 and 43 *Ulysses and the Sirens* by Herbert James Draper, Ferens Art Gallery, Hull. p3 and p 51 *The Forbidden World* by Rene Magritte, Private Collection. p4 and p 59 *Opera of the Seas* by Margaret MacDonald Mackintosh, The Fine art Society, London. p6 *A Mermaid Being Mobbed by Seagulls* by Giovanni Segantini, Bonhams, London. p7 *The Naiad* by John William Waterhouse, Roy Miles Gallery, London. p11 *Mermaids* by Beatrice Goldsmith, Chris Beetles Gallery, London. p12 *The Naiads at the arrival of Marie de Medici at Marseilles* by Peter Paul Rubens, Louvre, Paris/Giraudon. p15 *Little Mermaid*, by Hans Christian Andersen by E.S. Hardy, Private Collection. p21 *Mermaids at Play*, by Arnold Bocklin, Kunstmuseum, Basle. p23 and p34 *The Triumph of Venus* by Francesco Podesti, Galleria Nazionale d'Arte Moderna, Rome. p27 *A Sea Nymph* by Emile Jean Horace Vemet, Christie's, London. p30 *King Neptune* by Walter Crane, The Fine Art Society, London. p39 *The Five Mermaids*, by Evelyn de Morgan, The De Morgan Foundation, London. p41 *A Race with Mermaids and Titans* by Collier Smithers, Whitford & Hughes, London. p45 *The Siren* by Armand Pount, Barry Friedman, New York. p46 *Triumph of the Marine Venus* by Marco Ricci & Sebastiano Ricci, Christie's, London. p49 *Oberon and the Mermaid* by Sir Joseph Noel Paton, The Fine Art Society, London. p50 *The Mermaid* by Frederic K Leighton, City of Bristol Museum and Art Gallery. p53 *The Lady from the Sea* by Edvard Munch, Private Collection.

Archiv fur Kunst und Geschichte, Berlin.

p19 *Mermaids - Silverfish* by Gustav Klimt, Central Savings Bank, Vienna. p36 *Fair Melusine* by Julius Hubner, Posen National museum. p57 *Watersnakes I* by Gustav Klimt, Belvedere Gallery, Vienna. p58 *Galathea* by Gustave Moreau, Paris.

E.T. Archive, London.

p24 *The Mermaid*, illustrated by Edward Dulac, Victoria and Albert Museum. p28 *The Little Mermaid*, illustrated by Lorenz Frohlich. p32 Tiled panel with Merman and Mermaid, Palacio de los Fronteira, Lisbon.

The Arthur Rackham Society

p8 *Undine*, illustrated by Arthur Rackham. p13 *Sea Maid* from *A Midsummer's Nights Dream*, illustrated by Arthur Rackham. p63 "Clark Colville", illustrated by Arthur Rackham.

Private Collections

p9 *Ran from the Story of Siegfried*, illustrated by Peter Hurd. p16 illustrated by Harry Clarke. p25 *The Crown returns to the Queen of the Fairies* illustrated by H.J. Ford. p33 *The Sea Maiden with the Wicked Face*, illustrated by H. J. Ford. p35 *"Listen", said the Mermaid to the Prince* illustrated by H. J. Ford. p52 *Anghus*, illustrated by Stephen Reid. p61 *The Mermaid and the King*, illustrated by H. J. Ford. p62 *Sultan and the Merkid*, illustrated by William Heath Robinson.